Bond

Maths
Assessment Papers

8–9 years

**J M Bond and
Andrew Baines**

Nelson Thornes

First Published in 1973 by:
Thomas Nelson Ltd

This edition published in 2011 by:
Nelson Thornes Ltd
Delta Place
27 Bath Road
CHELTENHAM
GL53 7TH
United Kingdom

13 / 2

A catalogue record for this book is available from the British Library

ISBN 978 1 4085 1698 0

Page make-up by Tech Set Ltd

Printed in China by 1010 Printing International Ltd

Before you get started

What is Bond?

This book is part of the Bond Assessment Papers series for maths, which provides **thorough and continuous practice of all the key maths content** from ages five to thirteen. Bond's maths resources are ideal preparation for many different kinds of tests and exams – from SATs to 11+ and other secondary school selection exams.

What does this book cover?

It covers all the maths that a child of this age would be expected to learn and is fully in line with the National Curriculum for maths and the National Numeracy Strategy. One of the key features of Bond Assessment Papers is that each one practises **a wide variety of skills and question types** so that children are always challenged to think – and don't get bored repeating the same question type again and again. We think that variety is the key to effective learning. It helps children 'think on their feet' and cope with the unexpected.

The age given on the cover is for guidance only. As the papers are designed to be reasonably challenging for the age group, any one child may naturally find him or herself working above or below the stated age. The important thing is that children are always encouraged by their performance. Working at the right level is the key to this.

What does the book contain?

- **24 papers** – each one contains 40 questions.
- **Scoring devices** – there are score boxes in the margins and a Progress Chart on page 64. The chart is a visual and motivating way for children to see how they are doing. Encouraging them to colour in the chart as they go along and to try to beat their last score can be highly effective!
- **Next Steps** – advice on what to do after finishing the papers can be found on the inside back cover.
- **Answers** – located in an easily-removed central pull-out section.
- **Key maths words** – on page 1 you will find a glossary of special key words that are used in the papers. These are highlighted in bold each time that they appear These words are now used in the maths curriculum and children are expected to know them at this age.

How can you use this book?

One of the great strengths of Bond Assessment Papers is their flexibility. They can be used at home, school and by tutors to:

- provide regular maths practice in **bite-sized chunks**

    highlight strengths and weaknesses in the core skills

-

- identify **individual needs**
- set **homework**
- set **timed formal practice** tests – allow about 30 minutes.

It is best to start at the beginning and work though the papers in order.

What does a score mean and how can it be improved?

If children colour in the Progress Chart at the back, this will give you an idea of how they are doing. The Next Steps inside the back cover will help you to decide what to do next to help a child progress. We suggest that it is always valuable to go over any wrong answers with children.

Don't forget the website...!

Visit www.bond11plus.co.uk for lots of advice, information and suggestions on everything to do with Bond, exams, and helping children to do their best.

Key words

Some special maths words are used in this book. You will find them in **bold** each time they appear in the papers. These words are explained here.

area	the space inside a shape. Area is measured in square units, e.g. square centimetres (cm²) or square metres (m²).
cube	a solid shape whose faces are all squares, such as a child's building block
cuboid	a solid shape whose faces are either all rectangles, or rectangles and squares such as a cereal packet
digit	any single number. e.g. 4 has one digit, 37 has two digits, 437 has three digits
divisible	can be divided by. e.g. 4 is divisible by 2.
equilateral triangle	a triangle which has all its sides of the same length
heptagon	a shape with seven sides
hexagon	a shape with six sides
isosceles triangle	a triangle which has two sides the same length
mirror line	the line in which a shape can be reflected, like the reflection in a mirror
multiple	a number which another number multiplies into. e.g. 3, 6, 9, 12, 15, 60, 93 are multiples of 3.
net	the flat shape that a three-dimensional object, such as a box, will make if you open it out
octagon	a shape with 8 sides
parallelogram	a four-sided shape that has its opposite sides parallel
pentagon	a shape with five sides
perimeter	the distance round the outside of a shape
pictogram	a diagram that records something using pictures
polygon	a shape with three or more sides
product	the answer when you multiply two numbers together. e.g. The product of 4 and 2 is 8.
quadrilateral	a shape with 4 sides
round	means roughly or approximately e.g. 42 rounded to the nearest 10 is 40. 470 rounded to the nearest 100 is 500.
semicircle	a shape which is half a circle
square	a square is a rectangle with four equal sides
sum	the answer when you add two numbers together. The sum of 2 and 4 is 6.
symmetry	if a shape has symmetry it has one or more mirror lines like this:
tetrahedron	a solid shape with four triangular faces
Venn diagram	a chart for sorting information of different kinds

How many squares this size ☐ are there in each of the shapes below?

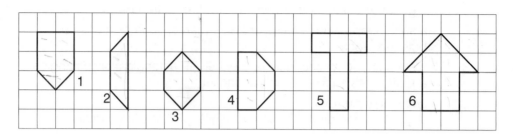

1 _____ 2 _____

3 _____ 4 _____

5 _____ 6 _____

◯ 6

7 Rachel is twice as old as Amy. If Amy is 7, how old is Rachel?

_____

◯ I

8 How many faces does this **cube** have?

_____

9 Underline the correct answer. Each face on the **cube** is:

a triangle   a square   a circle   a rectangle

10 How many faces does this **cuboid** have?

_____

11 Underline the correct answer. Each face on the **cuboid** is:

a triangle   a square   a circle   a rectangle

◯ 4

How many minutes are there between:

12 $\boxed{06:19}$ and $\boxed{06:30}$ _____

13 $\boxed{02:27}$ and $\boxed{02:50}$ _____

14 $\boxed{05:50}$ and $\boxed{06:10}$ _____

15 $\boxed{07:51}$ and $\boxed{08:00}$ _____

16 $\boxed{12:01}$ and $\boxed{12:40}$ _____

17 $\boxed{04:52}$ and $\boxed{05:10}$ _____

6

Underline the correct answer on each line.

18 $100 - 29 =$ 81   79   71 ✓   89   129

19 $56 \div 7 =$ 8 ✓   9   7   6   10

20 $47 + 35 =$ 72   73   81   71   82

21 $\frac{1}{2} + \frac{1}{2} =$ $\frac{1}{4}$ $\frac{1}{2}$ 1   2   4

4

22–23 Fill in the missing numbers on this number line.

$^-2$ $^-1$ _____   1   _____   3   4

24–25 Fill in the missing numbers on this number line.

$^-5$ $^-4$ _____ $^-2$ _____   0   1

26–29 Fill in the missing numbers on this number line.

_____ $^-6$ _____ $^-4$ _____ $^-2$ _____

8

Maria was born July 5th, 1994.   Anita was born April 19th, 1994.

Daley was born October 31st, 1994.   David was born November 8th, 1993.

30–31 _____ is the eldest and _____ is the youngest.

32–34 On July 5th 2006 Maria was _____ , Anita was _____

and _____ was 12.

35–37 $\xrightarrow{\times 6}$

12	
20	
40	

38–40 $\xrightarrow{+ 5}$

60	
80	
90	

○ 5

○ 6

Now go to the Progress Chart to record your score! Total ○ 40

Paper 2

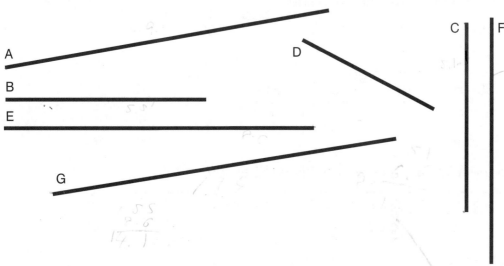

Measure each line and answer the questions.

1 The longest sloping line is _____.

2 The longest vertical line is _____.

3 The longest horizontal line is _____.

4 What is the difference in length between the two horizontal lines?
_____ cm

5 What is the difference in length between the two vertical lines?
_____ cm

6 The two vertical lines added together are _____ cm long.

7 The two horizontal lines added together are _____ cm long.

○ 7

8 What is the **product** of 5 and 7? _____ 35 ✓ ⓵

There are 60 children altogether in Class 2 and Class 3.

   9 If there are 32 in Class 2, how many are in Class 3? _____

George has three times as much money as Michael.

   10 Michael has 14p, so how much has George? _____ 42p ✓ ⓶

     312   123   321

11 In which number is the figure 1 a unit? _____

12 In which number is the figure 1 a ten? _____

13 In which number is the figure 1 a hundred? _____ ⓷

14 What number needs to go in the box? Write it in.

   4732 = ⎕4000 + 700 + 30 + 2

15 What number needs to go in the box? Write it in.

   5935 = 5000 + ⎕900 + 30 + 5

16 What number needs to go in the box? Write it in.

   3941 = 3000 + 900 + ⎕40 + 1

17 What number needs to go in the box? Write it in.

   5864 = 5000 + 800 + 60 + ⎕4

18 What number needs to go in the box? Write it in.

   9573 = ⎕9000 + 500 + 70 + 3

19 What number needs to go in the box? Write it in.

   1633 = 1000 + ⎕600 + 30 + 3

20 What number needs to go in the box? Write it in.

   7488 = 7000 + 400 + ⎕80 + 8   ⑦

21–22 Fill in the missing numbers on this number line.

13   15   17   19   ___   23   25   ___

2

Underline the correct answer in each line.

23	£1 – 11p	=	1p	89p	£1.11	99p	£1.01
24	8p + 6p + 7p	=	20p	22p	19p	21p	23p
25	66 + 26	=	92	87	82	83	93
26	105 ÷ 3	=	15	33	35	41	51
27	$\frac{1}{2}$ of 40	=	80	10	2	40	20
28	1000 ÷ 10	=	500	10	20	100	1000

6

Mum, Dad, Helen and Andrew went to the zoo.

Chartwell Zoo

Entrance: Adults   £2.50
Children £1.50
Monkey House: £1.00
Ice Cream: 60p

29 How much did it cost for all of them to go in? _____

30 How much did it cost for all of them to go in the monkey house?

_____

31 How much did it cost them to have an ice cream each? _____

32 How much did they spend at the zoo altogether? _____

4

There were 35 children in a class.

33–34 If the number of boys was one more than the number of girls, there
are ____ boys and ____ girls.

2

Here is part of a ruler.

35 How far is it from A to G?

36 How far is it from B to E?

37 How far is it from D to H?

38 How far is it from C to F?

39 What number, when divided by 9 gives an answer of 6?

40 How many times will 10 go into 200?

Now go to the Progress Chart to record your score!   Total   40

Paper 3

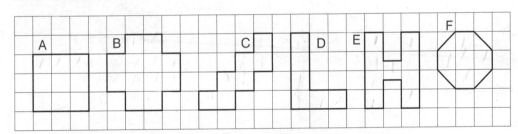

1 The area of shape A is _____ squares.

2 The area of shape B is _____ squares.

3 The area of shape C is _____ squares.

4 The area of shape D is _____ squares.

5 The area of shape E is _____ squares.

6 The area of shape F is _____ squares.

7 In every 2 weeks I spend 10 days at school. So in every 5 weeks
I spend _____ days at school.

8 In every 3 days I spend 4 hours reading. So in every _____ days I spend 20 hours reading.

9 With every box of cereal you get 4 tokens, and the toy you want requires 24 tokens.

How many boxes of cereal do you have to buy? _____

10 In every *Computer Kid* magazine you get 3 transfers. In 3 *Computer Kid* magazines you get _____ transfers.

(4)

11–15 Underline the numbers which can be divided exactly by 5.

52   25   40   24   45   54   60   51   15

(5)

16 Write in words 7001. _____

(1)

Church

Bus station

School

Castle

Railway station

N
NW   NE
W   E
SW   SE
S

In which direction is:

17 the school from the railway station? _____

18 the castle from the school? _____

19 the bus station from the school? _____

20 the church from the bus station? _____

21 the railway station from church? _____

22 the castle from the church? _____

23 the school from the bus station? _____

(7)

What number is halfway between:

24 50 and 70? _____

25 35 and 55? _____

26 25 and 35? _____

27 12 and 20? _____ (4)

28 Jane was born in 1998. Jock is 3 years older than Jane. In what year was he born? _____

29 Leanne was born in 1995. In what year was she 6? _____

30 Rehman was 12 in 1999. In what year was she born? _____ (3)

31–33 Reflect these shapes in the **mirror line**.

(3)

34 What is the biggest number you can make with these **digits**: 3, 6, 4, 8? _____

35 Now write it in words. _____

36 What is the biggest number you can make with these **digits**: 2, 3, 4, 0? _____

37 Now write it in words. _____

38 Write in figures three thousand, two hundred and fifty-four. _____ (5)

39 What is one quarter of 60? _____

40 How many minutes are there between 10:45 and 11:10? _____ (2)

Paper 4

1 73
    35
+ 98
_____

2   58
 × 6
_____

3 £6.98
+ £0.42
_____

3

4–9 Fill in the missing numbers to balance the scales.

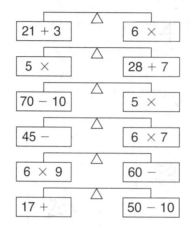

21 + 3	6 ×
5 ×	28 + 7
70 − 10	5 ×
45 −	6 × 7
6 × 9	60 −
17 +	50 − 10

6

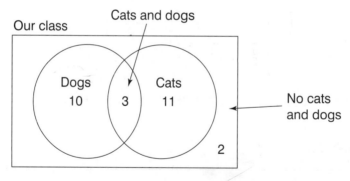

Our class

Cats and dogs

Dogs 10   3   Cats 11

No cats and dogs

2

Our class made this **Venn diagram** to show how many of us have cats and dogs.

10 How many children have dogs?

11 How many have cats?

12 How many have both a cat and a dog?

13 How many children haven't got a dog?

14 How many children haven't got a cat?

15 How many children are there in the class?

6

16 When a number was added to 16 the answer was 25. What was the number? _____

17 What temperature does this thermometer show? _____

-5 -4 -3 -2 -1 0 1 2 3 4

°C

18 Draw a circle around the lowest temperature: ⁻7°C,   ⁻9°C

19 Kay was 9 in 2000. In what year was she born? _____

20 Martin was born in December 1997 and Michael was born in January 1998.

Who is the elder? _____

This **pictogram** shows the number of children in our school.

Farm Lane	☀	☀	⸸								
High Street	☀	☀	☀	☀	☀	☀	☀	☀	☀	☀	
Birch Avenue	☀	☀	☀	☀	☀	☀	☀	⸸			
Riverside Road	☀	☀	☀	☀	☀	☀	☀	☀	☀	☀	☀
Manor Road	☀	☀	☀	☀	☀						

Key

☀ = 10 children

⸸ = 5 children

21 How many children are there in the school? _____

22 In which road or street do most children live? _____

23 Twice as many children live in the High Street as in _____

24 There are three times as many children in Birch Avenue as in

_____

25–28 Twenty more children come to our school. Five live in Farm Lane, 5 in Riverside Road and 10 in Birch Avenue. Show this on the **pictogram**.

29 How many will there now be in our school? _____

11

30 How much greater is 33 than 19? _____

31 I spent 77p and had 15p left. How much did I have at first? _____ p

32 What is the cost of 3 packets of crisps at 26p each? _____ p (3)

Look closely at the shape above.

33 How many **squares** does it contain? _____

34 How many rectangles does it contain? _____

35 How many triangles does it contain? _____ (3)

One question on each line has a different answer from the others.

Draw a line under it.

36   5 × 10   45 + 5   10 × 5   60 – 5   47 + 3

37   7 × 6   4 × 12   6 × 8   42 + 6   50 – 2   (2)

38 What number is 1 less than 300? _____

39 The number which is 2 more than 278 is _____

40 If I took 10 from 106 it would leave _____ (3)

Now go to the Progress Chart to record your score!   Total (40)

Paper 5

1 Draw a circle around the highest temperature: ⁻8 °C,   ⁻9 °C

2–3 Fill in the missing numbers on this number line.

_____   ⁻1   0   1   2   _____   4   (3)

12

Underline the correct answer in each line.

4	11 × 11	=	110	111	121	132	122
5	150 ÷ 30	=	50	5	30	20	55
6	70 − 39	=	41	49	39	109	31
7	$1\frac{1}{2}$ hours	=	75 min	90 min	45 min	85 min	15 min
8	1.5 kg	=	150 g	505 g	1500 g	1050 g	105 g
9	510 ÷ 5	=	21	102	120	12	121
10	150 cm	=	15 m	0.15 m	150 m	50 m	1.5 m

7

A

3 cm

7 cm

11 What is the **area** of rectangle A? _____ cm²

12 What is the **perimeter** of rectangle A? _____ cm

B

3 cm

17 cm

13 What is the **area** of rectangle B? _____ cm²

14 What is the **perimeter** of rectangle B? _____ cm

4

Fill in the missing number in each question.

15 3 + 4 + _____ = 10

16 5 + 1 − _____ = 4

17 3 + 3 + _____ = 9

3

13

18–22 Underline the numbers which are **divisible** by 7.

19   49   28   56   62   35   77   79

23–26 Underline the numbers which are **multiples** of 6.

36   72   26   96   56   24   28

Here is part of a centimetre ruler.

cm

27 How far is it from A to B?   _____

28 How far is it from C to D?   _____

29 How far is it from A to D?   _____

30 How far is it from B to F?   _____

31 How far is it from C to G?   _____

32 How far is it from E to G?   _____

Write the next two numbers in each line.

33–34   6   12   18   24   30   ____ ____

35–36   50   47   44   41   38   ____ ____

Underline the larger of each pair.

37 (6 × 10)   or   (3 × 22)

38 (5 × 20)   or   (11 × 10)

39 (10 × 10) or   (3 × 30)

40 (3 × 50)   or   (4 × 40)

Now go to the Progress Chart to record your score!   Total

1   37
   + 46
   ———

2   72
   − 39
   ———

3   36
   × 3
   ———

4   2)108

5–10 Complete the following bus timetable. Each bus takes the same amount of time to do the journey.

Bus	A	B	C
High Street	2:40	3:50	
Broad Lane		4:00	5:05
Market Place	2:55		
Kent Road	3:05		

Two shelves are 65 cm and 89 cm long.

11 What is their total length in metres? _____

12 What is the difference in their lengths in centimetres? _____

13 What fraction of the circle is spotted? _____

14 What fraction is striped? _____

15 What fraction is plain? _____

16 How many times larger is the spotted part than the striped part? _____

15

17–23 Complete the empty brackets in this multiplication table.

×	4	5	( )
	(5)	10	( )
	12	( )	18
	( )	20	( )
	20	(30)	

24 164 × 4 = _____

25 182 × 6 = _____

Put the correct sign in the spaces.

26–27   3 _____ 4 = 6 _____ 1

28–29   5 _____ 4 = 2 _____ 7

30–31   3 _____ 3 = 8 _____ 1

32–33   8 _____ 1 = 5 _____ 2

This **pictogram** shows how the children in Class 4 come to school.

Key

 = 1 child

34 How many children are there in the class? _____

35 How many more walk than come by car? _____

36 How many more come by car than by bus? _____

37 How many children don't come by bus? _____

38 How many more children walk than come by bus? _____

39 How many children don't come by train? _____

40 How many times can I take 9 from 54? _____

Paper 7

1 345 ÷ 5 = _____

2 345 + 456 = _____

3 321 × 3 = _____

⬤ 3

4–6 Fill in the missing numbers on this number line.

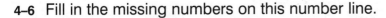

‾7   _____   ‾5   _____   ‾3   _____   ‾1

⬤ 3

7 Draw a circle around the highest temperature: ‾17°C,   ‾29°C

8–12 Put these temperature in order, lowest first.

0°C,   ‾4°C,   ‾7°C,   3°C,   ‾1°C   _____

⬤ 6

13 My watch was 5 minutes fast. It showed 10:30.
What was the right time?   _____ : _____

⬤ I

Afternoon school begins at 1:30 and finishes at 3:35.

14 For how long do we work in the afternoon?   _____ hr   _____ min

15 What change should I have from £1.00 if I spent 67p?   _____ p

⬤ 2

16–20 Change this recipe for ginger nuts for 6 people to a recipe for 12 people for a party.

6 people	
125 g	flour
30 g	fat
75 g	sugar
30 ml	treacle
1 teaspoon	ground ginger

12 people	
_____ g	flour
_____ g	fat
_____ g	sugar
_____ ml	treacle
_____ teaspoons	ground ginger

⬤ 5

Underline the question in each line which does not have the same answer as the others.

21   4 × 3   6 × 2   12 × 1   4 × 2

(17)

22	4×4	8×2	1×16	3×5
23	6×5	9×4	10×3	15×2
24	$20 \div 4$	$25 \div 6$	$10 \div 2$	$15 \div 3$
25	$16 - 7$	$18 \div 2$	3×3	$4 + 6$
26	$36 \div 3$	6×3	$25 - 7$	$7 + 11$

6

27 Which town is the furthest away from Boxo? _____

28 Which town is the nearest to Boxo? _____

29 How much further is it from Boxo to Farway than it is from
Boxo to Manley? _____

3

30–31 Underline the smallest number and circle the largest.

   5.7   4.8   7.5   8.4   4.5

2

32 Convert metres into centimetres: 7.45 m = _____ cm

33 **Round** to the nearest pound: £7.49   = £ _____

34 Convert centimetres into metres: 824 cm = _____ m

35 Write 345p in £.   345p   = £ _____

4

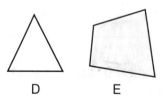

A   B   C   D   E

36–37 Shade in the **quadrilaterals** above.

A   B   C   D   E

38–40 Shade in the **pentagons** above.

5

Now go to the Progress Chart to record your score!   **Total**   **40**

Paper 8

1 How many pence in £1.25?   _____

2 How many pence in £0.29?   _____

2

A _____

B _____

C _____

D _____

E _____

F _____

3 Line A is _____ cm long.

4 Line B is _____ cm long.

5 Line C is _____ cm long.

6 Line D is _____ cm long.

7 Line E is _____ cm long.

8 Line F is _____ cm long.

9 What is the difference in length between the longest and
the shortest line?   _____ cm

10–11 Lines A and B put together would be the same length as lines _____
and _____ put together.

9

A   B   C

12–14   A has _____ ml.   B has _____ ml.   C has _____ ml.

How many ml of water would you have to add to each jug so that each one holds half a litre?

15–17   A needs _____ ml.   B needs _____ ml.   C needs _____ ml.   ◯ 6

18   What is the remainder when 40 is divided by 6?   _____   ◯ 1

In the number 1234:   how many tens are there?   3

how many hundreds are there?   2

19   In the number 135:   how many tens are there?   _____

20   how many hundreds are there?   _____

21   In the number 1247:   how many units are there?   _____

22   how many hundreds are there?   _____

23   In the number 2439:   how many tens are there?   _____

24   how many thousands are there?   _____   ◯ 6

25   What is $\frac{1}{2}$ of 22?   _____

26 $\frac{1}{3}$ of 24 is   _____

27 $\frac{1}{4}$ of 20 is   _____

28   What is $\frac{1}{5}$ of 15?   _____

29 $\frac{1}{10}$ of 40 is   _____

30 $\frac{1}{3}$ of 27 is   _____   ◯ 6

What are the names of these shapes?

Use the following words to help you:

sphere   triangular prism   **cuboid**   **cube**   cylinder

31 _____

32 _____

33 _____

34 _____

35 _____

36 John is 120.5 cm tall. James is 4.5 cm shorter.

How tall is James?   _____

A   40 cm

60 cm

37 What is the **area** of rectangle A?   _____ cm^2

38 What is the **perimeter** of rectangle A?   _____ cm

B   44 m

60 m

39 What is the **area** of rectangle B?   _____ m^2

40 What is the **perimeter** of rectangle B?   _____ m

Now go to the Progress Chart to record your score!   Total   40

21

Paper 9

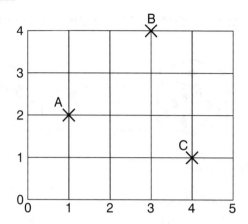

A is 1 square along and 2 squares up from (0,0).

1–2 B is _____ squares along and _____ squares up from (0,0).

3–4 C is _____ squares along and _____ square up from (0,0).

A is at the point (1,2).

5 B is at the point (_____, _____).

6 C is at the point (_____, _____).

7 D is at the point (2,3). Mark it on the grid above.

8 E is at the point (5,0). Mark it on the grid above.

 8

9   4.9
+ 7.5

_____

10   3.9
× 8

_____

2

11 Share 20 cherries among 5 children. They have _____ each.

12 How many glasses holding $\frac{1}{2}$ litre could be filled from a jug which holds $7\frac{1}{2}$ litres?   _____

13 Sally missed the 9:25 a.m. bus. The next one is 17 minutes later. At what time is the next bus?   _____

14 I had 9p after spending 24p. How much did I have at first?   _____

15 Aziz walks 4 km each day. In November he walks _____ km.   **5**

22

Here is a bar chart which shows the number of hours of sunshine we had each day in the last week of June.

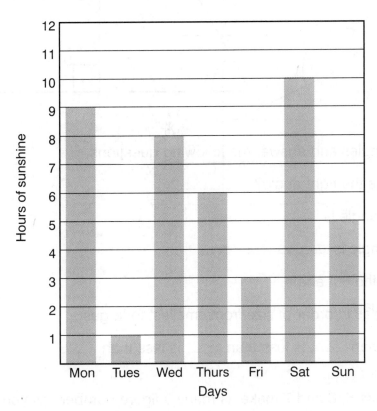

16–17 Which 2 days added together had the same amount of sunshine as Saturday?

_____ and _____

18 It rained on only one day in the week. On which day did it probably rain?

_____

19–21 On which 3 days together did the total sunshine equal that of Monday?

_____ , _____ and _____

22 How many days had fewer than 6 hours of sunshine? _____

23 How many days had more than 8 hours of sunshine? _____

24 What was the total hours of sunshine for the week? _____

25–30 The sunniest day was Saturday. Write the other days in the order of sunniest day to least sunny day.

Saturday, _____ , _____ , _____ ,

_____ , _____ , _____ .

15

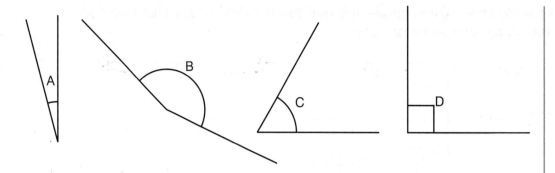

Look at the above angles and answer the following questions.

31 Which angle is the right angle? _____

32 The smallest angle is _____ .

33 The largest angle is _____ .

34 _____ is the 60° angle.

35–38 Place the angles in order of size from smallest to largest.

_____ is less than _____ is less than _____ is less than _____.

8

39 Using the **digits** 5, 6 and 7 make as many 3-figure numbers as you can.

_____ _____ _____ _____ _____ _____

40 Now take away the smallest from the largest. _____

2

Now go to the Progress Chart to record your score!   Total   40

Paper 10

1 Write the correct number in the box.

231 ⟶ [   ]
       75 less is

2 Write the correct number in the box.

[   ] ⟶ 260
       62 less is

2

3 Put these numbers in order, smallest to largest.

7536   6537   5736   6573

_____   _____   _____   _____

Look at this grid.

4 How many **squares** of this size are in the grid?   _____

5 How many **squares** of this size are in the grid?   _____

6 How many **squares** of this size are in the grid?   _____

7 What is the total number of **squares** in the grid?   _____

8 What is the smallest number you can make with these **digits**: 3, 5, 4, 9?   _____

9 Now write it in words.

_____

10 What is the largest number you can make with these **digits**: 3, 5, 4, 9?   _____

11 Now write it in words.

_____

12 What is the smallest number you can make with these **digits**: 9, 5, 8, 6, 1?   _____

13 Now write it in words.

_____

14 What is the largest number you can make with these **digits**: 9, 5, 8, 6, 1? _____

15 Now write it in words.

_____

16 Write in figures one thousand, four hundred and eighty-nine. _____

17 Write in figures seven thousand and eighty-nine. _____

Here is a **pictogram** which shows what kind of books are liked most by children in Readwell School.

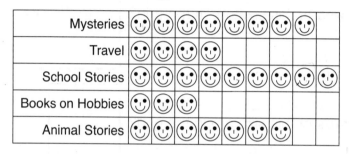

Key ☺ = 10 children

18 Which type of book is most popular? _____

19 Which type of book is least popular? _____

20 How many children are in the school? _____

21 Which kind of book is twice as popular as travel books? _____

22 How many more children like mysteries than animal stories? _____

23 How many more children prefer school stories to travel books? _____

6

Underline the right answer in each line.

24 Round £3.70 to the nearest pound: £3 £4 £7 £10 £70

25 Round £26.01 to the nearest pound: £20 £25 £26 £27 £30

2

26 £
   4.39
− 1.72
_____

27 £
   0.27
×   5
_____

2

Ring the correct answer.

28 When you add together two odd numbers the answer is:

an odd number   an even number

29 If you add together two even numbers the answer is:

an odd number   an even number

30 If you add together three even numbers the answer is:

an odd number   an even number

31 If you add together three odd numbers the answer is:

an odd number   an even number   4

32 What is the **sum** of the even numbers between 3 and 7?   _____

33 What is the difference between 7 and 19?   _____   2

34 How many times can I take £1.25 from £6.25?   _____   1

Write the correct fraction in each space.

35 Shaded   _____

36 Unshaded   _____

37 Shaded   _____

38 Unshaded   _____

39 Shaded   _____

40 Unshaded   _____

6

Paper 11

1 Sally left home at 08:52 and arrived at school at 09:01.

   How long did it take her to walk to school? _____

2 If I spent 23p and had 18p left, how much had I at first? _____ p

3 How many children are there altogether in a school if
   there are 197 boys and 165 girls? _____ ③

Here are four regular pizzas. One whole, one cut in halves, one in thirds and
one in sixths.

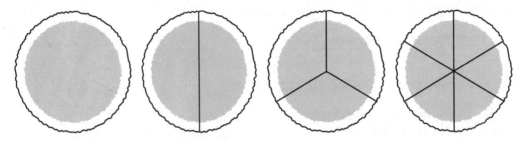

4 How many $\frac{1}{6}$s make 1 whole? _____

5 How many $\frac{1}{6}$s make $\frac{1}{3}$? _____

6 How many $\frac{1}{6}$s make $\frac{1}{2}$? _____

7 How many $\frac{1}{3}$s make 1 whole? _____

8 How many $\frac{1}{6}$s make $\frac{2}{3}$? _____ ⑤

9
```
   369
   425
 + 264
 ─────
```

10
```
   204
 ×   8
 ─────
```

②

11 How many times can I take 9 from 99? _____

12 From the **digits** 4, 5 and 6 make a number so that the
    5 is the hundred and the 4 is the unit. _____

13 Write in figures two thousand and twenty. _____

14 How many times can I take 8 from 56? _____ 4

15–17 Shade in the **hexagons**.

18–24 Here are the ingredients for a meal for 1 person.

Jacket Potato with Leeks and Cheese for 1 person	
1 large (about 200 g)	potato
10 g	butter
1 tablespoon	milk
2 (about 150 g)	leeks
40 g	grated cheese

Increase the measurements to change it to a recipe for 4 people.

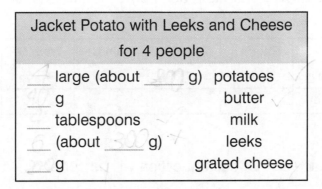

Jacket Potato with Leeks and Cheese for 4 people	
___ large (about ___ g)	potatoes
___ g	butter
___ tablespoons	milk
___ (about ___ g)	leeks
___ g	grated cheese

7

25–26 18 is half of _____, and three times as much as _____ .

27 How many jars of Bovo, each costing 75p, can I buy with £3.75? _____ 3

This clock shows the correct time.

How fast or slow are the clocks below?

Write the number of minutes and ring the correct word for each clock.

28–29 _____ minutes   fast

                             slow

30–31 _____ minutes   fast

                             slow

32–33 _____ minutes   fast

                             slow

6

34–38 Each train takes 1 hr 10 min to reach Fordby. Write what time each one arrives.

	Train A	Train B	Train C	Train D	Train E
Leaves Bunmouth at	10:00	11:30	12:50	13:55	15:10
Arrives at Fordby at					

5

Put a sign in each space so that each question will be correct.

39   5 _____ 2 = 2 _____ 1

40   4 _____ 4 = 10 _____ 2

2

Paper 12

1 It is now 2:37 p.m. In half an hour's time it will be _____ : _____ p.m.

2 What time is a quarter of an hour before midnight? _____ : _____ p.m.

3 Six minutes after 10:45 is _____ : _____

£1.50	£3.25	£2.75	£1.25	£2.95
A	B	C	D	E

4–5 Which two toys could you buy with £3.00? _____ and _____

6 How much would it cost to buy the bat and the football? £ _____

7 How much change would you have from £3.00 if you bought a van? £ _____

8 How much change would you have from £5.00 if you bought a boat? £ _____

9 How much would it cost to buy all the toys? £ _____

10 How much would it cost to buy a van and two bats? £ _____

11–14 Draw the lines of **symmetry** in each of the following shapes.

The first one has been done for you.

15–26 The table below should show the important times in the morning at Greenway Primary School.

Each lesson is half an hour long. Break lasts 15 minutes. Lessons begin at 09:30.

Fill in the correct times.

	Begins	**Ends**
First lesson		
Second lesson		
Break		
Third lesson		
Fourth lesson		
Fifth lesson		

12

27–30 Join each three-dimensional object on the left with its **net** on the right by drawing a line.

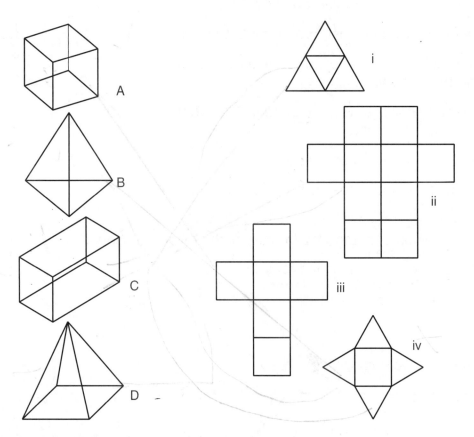

4

31 What is the difference between 1 litre and 850 ml? _____ ml

1

The children in a swimming club made this **pictogram**.

It shows how many children of each age group could swim.

Age 7	🧍 🧍								
Age 8	🧍 🧍 🧍 🧍								
Age 9	🧍 🧍 🧍 🧍 🧍 🧍 🧍 ⸸								
Age 10	🧍 🧍 🧍 🧍 🧍 🧍 🧍 🧍 🧍								
Age 11	🧍 🧍 🧍 🧍 🧍 🧍 🧍 🧍 ⸸								

Key

🧍 = 2 children

⸸ = 1 child

32 How many children in the club can swim? _____

33 How many more 10-year-olds than 8-year-olds can swim? _____

Swimming group A has all the 10-year-olds and 11-year-olds.

Swimming group B has all the younger children.

34 Which is the larger group? _____

35 How many more are in this group? _____

A season ticket for the swimming baths costs £5.00 each.

36 If all the children bought a season ticket, what would
    be the total cost? _____

Last Thursday there was a 100 m race. Two of the 9-year-olds entered along
with all the 10- and 11-year-olds.

37 How many were in the race? _____

38 The rest of the children entered the 50 m race.
    How many were in this race? _____   7

39 What is the remainder when 28 is divided by 5? _____

40 What is the remainder when 28 is divided by 6? _____   2

Paper 13

Use two of the numbers in the brackets to complete the following **sums**. Do not use the same combination twice.

1–2 _____ + _____ + 9 = 12   (1, 2, 3, 4, 5, 6, 7, 8)

3–4 _____ + _____ + 8 = 12   (1, 2, 3, 4, 5, 6, 7)

5–6 _____ + _____ + 7 = 12   (1, 2, 3, 4, 5, 6)

7–8 _____ + _____ + 7 = 12   (1, 2, 3, 4, 5, 6)

9–10 _____ + _____ + 6 = 12   (1, 2, 3, 4, 5)

11–12 _____ + _____ + 6 = 12   (1, 2, 3, 4, 5)

13–14 _____ + _____ + 5 = 12   (1, 2, 3, 4)

14

15–18 Use the numbers in the brackets below only once to make each side of the square add up to 12. You can use the **sums** above to help you.

(1, 2, 3, 5)

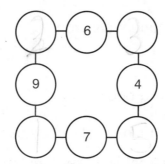

4

19–23 Make these shapes look the same on each side of the **mirror line**.

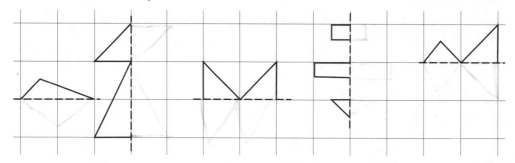

5

Put a sign in each space so that each question will be correct.

24 6 _____ 6 = 4 _____ 3

25 4 _____ 5 = 3 _____ 3

26 6 _____ 2 = 3 _____ 1

27 7 _____ 4 = 4 _____ 1

28 8 _____ 2 = 5 _____ 1

29 7 _____ 1 = 4 _____ 4

This bar chart shows how many people got on a bus at each of the four stops in the centre of the town.

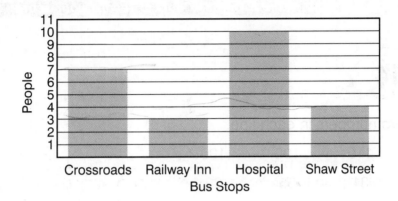

30 How many people got on the bus altogether? _____

31 How many more people got on at the hospital than at the Railway Inn? _____

32 How many more people got on at the crossroads than at Shaw Street? _____

33 How many more people got on at Shaw Street than at the Railway Inn? _____

34 If all the people who got on the bus paid 60p each, how much was this altogether? £ _____

A quarter of the passengers got off the bus at the next stop and 3 more got on.

35 Now how many passengers would be on the bus? _____

Mrs Andrews 18 kg   Mr Bell 8.6 kg   Mrs Clark 17.1 kg   Mr Dring 21.4 kg   Mr Eliot 14.8 kg

Passengers cannot take more than 16 kg on the plane.

36–37 Who was allowed to take all their luggage with them?

_____ and _____

38 Whose luggage is the heaviest? _____

39 How much over 16 kg is his case? _____

40 How much extra weight would Mr Bell be allowed to
put in his case to make it up to 16 kg? _____

5

Now go to the Progress Chart to record your score! **Total** **40**

Paper 14

Write the next two numbers in each line.

1–2	115	110	105	100	_____	_____
3–4	27	31	35	39	_____	_____
5–6	543	538	533	528	_____	_____
7–8	213	219	225	231	_____	_____
9–10	66	77	88	99	_____	_____

10

11 How many times can I take 7 from 98? _____

1

Underline the correct answer in each line.

12 12×11 = 112   121   123   132   144

13 $400 \div 20$ = 40   20   200   400   4

14 $101 - 89$ = 12   11   21   23   22

15 $\frac{1}{2}$ hour = 15 min   20 min   30 min   40 min   45 min

16 70×40 = 280   2800   1100   240   470

17 $603 \div 3$ = 21   31   301   201   210

6

18 My watch is 9 minutes slow. It shows 5 minutes to 11.
What is the right time? _11 : 04_

19 When a number is taken away from 21 the answer is 8.
What is the number? _____

2

20
```
   27
   68
   49
 + 36
 ─────
```

21
```
   403
 ×  70
 ─────
```

A
↕ 3 m
←──────── 200 m ────────→

22 What is the **area** of rectangle A? _____ m²

23 What is the **perimeter** of rectangle A? _____ m

B
↕ 30 m
←──────── 200 m ────────→

24 What is the **area** of rectangle B? _____ m²

25 What is the **perimeter** of rectangle B? _____ m

26 How many times bigger is the **area** of rectangle B than the **area** of rectangle A? _____

27 By how much is the **perimeter** of B bigger than the **perimeter** of A? _30_

28 From the figures 7, 8 and 9 make a number so that 9 is the hundred and 8 is the unit. _987_

29 What is the **product** of 10 and 100? _1000_

Write the answers to the following questions.

30 $12 \times 8 = 10 \times 8 + 2 \times 8 =$ _____

31 $15 \times 7 = 10 \times 7 + 5 \times 7 =$ _____

32 $18 \times 5 = 10 \times 5 + 8 \times 5 =$ _____

33 $16 \times 9 = 10 \times 9 + 6 \times 9 =$ _____

My brother has 40 counters.

18 are yellow, 15 are green and the rest are blue.

34 How many are blue?

35 How many times can I take 6 from 72?

7
_12_

2

To make a rosette you need 15 cm of ribbon.

36 How many could you make with a metre of ribbon?

_1_

37 How much ribbon would be left over?

_____

2

38 What is the **sum** of the odd numbers smaller than 10?

_25_

1

39 What needs to be added to change 5864 to 7864?

40 What needs to be subtracted to change 6842 to 6342?

5
_8_

2

Now go to the Progress Chart to record your score!   **Total**   **40**

Paper 15

1–2 Fill in the missing numbers on this number line.

⁻22   ⁻21   _____   ⁻19   _____   ⁻17   ⁻16

2

3 How many weeks are there in 28 days?

_____

1

Here is part of a centimetre ruler.

     A   B C D   E F G   H I J   K

19   20   21   22   23   24   25   26   27   28

4 How far is it from A to B?

5 How far is it from D to G?

6 How far is it from G to K?

7 How far is it from F to H? _____

8 What is the distance between A and C? _____

9 How far is it from A to K? _____

10 How far is it from B to J? _____

11 What is the distance from C to F? _____ ⬤ 8

12 The film lasted 153 min, which is _____ min to the nearest 100 min.

13 Oxton to Cowster is 197 miles, which is _____ miles to the nearest 10 miles.

14 The return trip (from Oxton to Cowster and back) is _____ miles to the nearest 10 miles. ⬤ 3

A   B   C   D   E

15–17 Shade in the **quadrilaterals**. ⬤ 3

18 What is the **product** of 6 and 21? _____

You start with 16 eggs. Half are broken so you throw them away. Half of the unbroken eggs are too old so you throw them away.

19 You are now left with _____ good eggs.

20 Twice nine is _____ ⬤ 3

Our class

Black shoes   11   5   8   Grey socks

3

21 How many children are in the class? _____

22 How many children are wearing grey socks? _____

23 How many are wearing black shoes? _____

24 _____ children are wearing grey socks and black shoes.

25 How many children are not wearing black shoes? _____

26 _____ are not wearing grey socks.

6

27 I spend 27p. What change should I receive if I give
the shopkeeper £1.00? _____ p

The time is 5 to 8. How fast or slow are these clocks?

Write the number of minutes and ring the correct word for each clock

28–29 _____ minutes   fast

slow

30–31 _____ minutes   fast

slow

32–33 _____ minutes   fast

slow

34–35 _____ minutes   fast

slow

36 What needs to be added/subtracted to change 7812 to 7212?

_____

37 What needs to be added/subtracted to change 6324 to 6354?

_____

38 What is the largest number you can make with these **digits**:
2, 5, 8, 6, 5? _____

39 Now write it in words.

_____

40 Write in figures four thousand, one hundred and twenty. _____

1–3 What fraction of the board is shaded? Underline the correct answers.

$\frac{1}{2}$ $\frac{1}{3}$ $\frac{1}{6}$ $\frac{1}{12}$ $\frac{2}{3}$ $\frac{2}{6}$ $\frac{2}{12}$ $\frac{3}{6}$ $\frac{3}{12}$ $\frac{6}{12}$

4–5 What fraction of the paperclips has been ringed? Underline all the correct answers.

$\frac{1}{2}$ $\frac{1}{3}$ $\frac{1}{4}$ $\frac{1}{6}$ $\frac{2}{3}$ $\frac{2}{4}$ $\frac{2}{6}$ $\frac{3}{4}$ $\frac{3}{6}$

6 Which fraction is larger: $\frac{1}{2}$ or $\frac{1}{4}$? _____ 6

Put a circle round the correct answer.

7 0.25 = $\frac{1}{2}$ $\frac{2}{5}$ $\frac{1}{4}$ $\frac{25}{10}$

8 0.1 = $\frac{1}{2}$ $\frac{1}{1}$ $\frac{1}{10}$ $\frac{1}{100}$ 2

9 In a sponsored swim, Kevin's dad says he will pay 50p per length.

Kevin swims 13 lengths, so his dad has to pay   £ _____ 1

10 Which town is furthest away from Nottingham? _____

11 Which town is nearest to Nottingham? _____

12 Brighton is further away from Nottingham than Southampton is by _____

13 Cardiff is further away from Nottingham than Leeds is by _____

14 What is the distance from Nottingham to Southampton to the nearest 10 km? _____ km

15 What is the distance from Nottingham to Leeds to the nearest 10 km? _____ km   ◯ 6

16 Write in figures: eight thousand and eighteen. _____   ◯ 1

17–19 Carefully draw the hands on the clocks on the right so they show the same times as those on the left.

12:30

Remember that the hour hand is shorter than the minute hand.

3

20 $\frac{1}{2}$ of 26 = _____

21 $\frac{2}{3}$ of 21 = _____

22 $\frac{3}{4}$ of 16 = _____

3

23 6 paper chains at 80p cost £ _____ .

24 6 strands of tinsel at 85p cost £ _____ .

25 How many Christmas cards, at 45p can I buy with £2.00? _____

3

Alison weighs 39 kg, Christopher weighs 37.5 kg and Rachel weighs 41.7 kg.

26 Alison and Christopher together weigh _____ kg

27 How much heavier is Alison than Christopher? _____ kg

28 Christopher and Rachel together weigh _____ kg

3

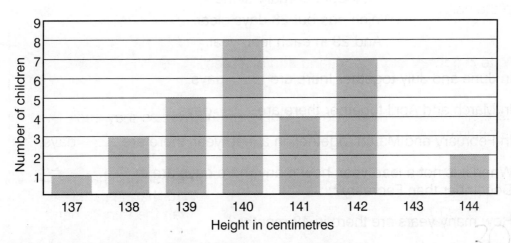

29 How many children are shown on the bar chart? _____

30 How many children are 143 cm tall? _____

31 How many more children are 140 cm tall than are 138 cm? _____

32 How many children are less than 140 cm tall? _____

33 How many children are more than 140 cm tall? _____ ◯ 5

34 4 m 25 cm + 5 m 75 cm = _____ m

35 8 m 36 cm + 7 m 68 cm = _____ m

36 5 m 0 cm − 2 m 45 cm = _____ m

37 6 m 10 cm − 2 m 70 cm = _____ m ◯ 4

38–39 If 5 m of material costs £6.00, 1 m will cost _____
and 11 m will cost _____. ◯ 2

40 How many $\frac{1}{2}$ hour lessons are there between 09:30 and 12:00? _____ ◯ 1

Now go to the Progress Chart to record your score!   Total ◯ 40

Paper 17

Thirty days has September,
April, June and November.
All the rest have 31,
Except February alone
Which has but 28 days clear,
And 29 in each leap year.

1 In June and July together there are _____ days.

2 In March and April together there are _____ days.

3 In February and March together, in a leap year, there are _____ days.

4 When it is not a leap year, how many more days are in
December than February? _____

5 How many years are there in 48 months? _____

6 How many years in a millennium? _____ ◯ 6

7 What fraction of the picture above is dotted? _____

8 What fraction is striped? _____

9 What fraction is plain? _____

10 What fraction has crosses? _____ ⟩ 4

11 If three pencils cost 99p what will be the cost of two pencils? _____ p

12 What is the **product** of 7 and 6? _____

13 If 12 books cost £66.00 what is the cost of one book? _____ ⟩ 3

Put a sign in each space so that each question will be correct.

14–15 7 ⨰ 1 = 4 __ 4

16–17 3 __ 7 = 5 __ 2

18–19 6 __ 1 = 8 __ 1

20–21 6 __ 4 = 2 __ 12

22–23 4 __ 4 = 10 __ 6

24–25 12 __ 3 = 8 __ 2

26–27 2 __ 7 = 15 __ 1

28–29 3 __ 1 = 7 __ 4 ⟩ 16

30   428
   × 7
   _____

31   3.29
   × 6
   _____

32   3.24
   × 7
   _____
⟩ 3

This diagram shows that one whole can be divided into thirds, sixths and twelfths.

1 Whole											
$\frac{1}{3}$				$\frac{1}{3}$				$\frac{1}{3}$			
$\frac{1}{6}$		$\frac{1}{6}$		$\frac{1}{6}$		$\frac{1}{6}$		$\frac{1}{6}$		$\frac{1}{6}$	
$\frac{1}{12}$	$\frac{1}{12}$	$\frac{1}{12}$	$\frac{1}{12}$	$\frac{1}{12}$	$\frac{1}{12}$	$\frac{1}{12}$	$\frac{1}{12}$	$\frac{1}{12}$	$\frac{1}{12}$	$\frac{1}{12}$	$\frac{1}{12}$

33 How many $\frac{1}{3}$s make 1? _____

34 How many $\frac{1}{12}$s make $\frac{2}{3}$? _____

35 How many $\frac{1}{6}$s make $\frac{1}{3}$? _____

36 How many $\frac{1}{12}$s make 1? _____

37 How many $\frac{1}{6}$s make $\frac{2}{3}$? _____

38 How many $\frac{1}{6}$s make 1? _____

39 How many $\frac{1}{12}$s make $\frac{5}{6}$? _____

40 How many $\frac{1}{3}$s make $\frac{8}{12}$? _____   ◯ 8

Now go to the Progress Chart to record your score!   Total ◯ 40

Paper 18

Write the next two numbers in each of the following lines.

1–2	£1.75	£1.50	£1.25	£1.00	_____	_____
3–4	30p	36p	42p	48p	_____	_____
5–6	2015	2025	2035	2045	_____	_____
7–8	$\frac{1}{2}$	1	$1\frac{1}{2}$	2	_____	_____
9–10	1 day	20 hr	16 hr	12 hr	_____	_____
11–12	132	140	148	156	_____	_____

◯ 12

13	m	14	m	15	m l
	22.5		26.5		38.9
	+ 18.6		+ 36.5		+ 43.8

Fill in the missing numbers in each of these questions.

16 $4 \times \underline{} = 12$

17 $2 + 3 + \underline{} = 11$

18 $5 \times 6 = \underline{}$

19 $12 - \underline{} = 8$

20 $24 + \underline{} = 30$

21 How many years in 60 months? _____

Pauline bought a book for £4.75 and some writing paper for £1.80.

22 How much did she spend? £ _____

23 How much change would she have from £10.00? £ _____

24 The school hall has 32 rows of chairs and there are 20 chairs in each row. How many chairs are there altogether? _____

25 What is the **product** of 7 and 12? _____

26–29 $\xrightarrow{\times 4}$

14	
21	
16	
23	

30–34 $\xrightarrow{\div 6}$

54	
36	
42	
150	
186	

35 How many erasers for 5p each could you buy with £6.85? _____

36 $50 \times 1 = 60 - \underline{}$

37 $20 \times 0 = 7 - \underline{}$

Put the hands on these clocks.

38 25 past 2

39 $\frac{1}{4}$ to 10

40 10 past 7

◯ 3

Now go to the Progress Chart to record your score! Total ◯ 40

Paper 19

1–2 Underline the smallest and circle the largest.

22p, £2, £0.02, £2.22, £2.02 202p

3–4 Underline the smallest and circle the largest.

623　　632　　642　　640　　622　　624

◯ 4

5 **Round** to the nearest pound: £9.66 = £_____

6 Write 964p in £. 964p = £_____

7 Write metres in centimetres: 34.4 m = _____ cm

◯ 3

8 The age of Bridget, Bob and Sarah add up to 24 years.

If Bob is 8 and Bridget is 7, how old is Sarah? _____

◯ 1

One side of a **square** room is 6 m.

9 How far is it all round? _____

10 What is the **area** of the **square** floor? _____

◯ 2

Here is a timetable for Wednesday morning.

Mathematics	09:15–09:45
Music	09:45–10:30
Break	10:30–10:50
History	10:50–11:25
Games	11:25–12:00

11 We do mathematics for _____ min.

12 Break is _____ min long.

13 We play games for _____ min.

14 We spend _____ min having our music lesson.

15 How long is the history lesson? _____ min.

16 From 09:15 to 12:00 is _____ hour _____ min.

17 London to Leeds is 283 miles, which is _____ miles to the nearest 100 miles.

18 The return trip (to Leeds and back) is _____ miles to the nearest 100 miles.

19–20 The fuel tank in a truck holds 151 litres, which is _____ litres to the nearest 10 litres and _____ litres to the nearest 100 litres.

21 Fill in the missing number in the brackets on this number line.

$^-5$ \qquad (_____) \qquad\qquad\qquad\qquad 1

22 Put these temperatures in order, lowest first.

5 °C \qquad $^-14$ °C \qquad $^-1$ °C \qquad _____ _____ _____

Underline the two questions in each line which give the answer.

23–24	$13 =$	$9 + 3$	7×2	$11 + 2$	$19 - 6$	$14 + 1$
25–26	$6\frac{1}{2} =$	$12\frac{1}{2} - 6\frac{1}{2}$	$10 - 3\frac{1}{2}$	$4 + 2$	$5\frac{1}{4} + 2\frac{1}{4}$	$4\frac{1}{4} + 2\frac{1}{4}$
27–28	$5 =$	$10 - 10$	20×5	$18 - 13$	$15 - 5$	5×1

6

2

2

1

1

6

29	88	30	709	31	709
	77		× 8		× 80
	+ 66				

⟨3⟩

Here is a **pictogram** which shows the number of people who had tea at Meg's Café last Thursday.

 represents 5 people having tea.

32 How many people had tea at Meg's Café between 2 p.m. and 4 p.m.? _____

33 How many had tea between 4 p.m. and 6 p.m.? _____

34 How many more people had tea between 4 p.m. and 5 p.m., than between 2 p.m. and 3 p.m.? _____

35 If the café charged £4 for a tea how much money was taken last Thursday? _____

Twice the number of people who had tea at Meg's Café on Thursday had tea there on Saturday.

36 How many were there on Saturday? _____ ⟨5⟩

Look at this **sum** carefully.

32 + 49   = 81

Now use it to help you with the following questions.

37 81 − 32   = _____   38 132 + 149 = _____

39 181 − 132 = _____   40 532 + 349 = _____   ⟨4⟩

Now go to the Progress Chart to record your score!   Total   ⟨40⟩

Paper 20

Fill in the missing numbers so that each question will be correct.

1
```
   2_
 + 46
 ────
   69
 ────
```

2
```
  40
 - __
 ───
  22
```

3
```
  __
 × 3
 ───
 105
```

○ 3

4 Rakesh gets £2.50 pocket money a week.

   If he saves half of it, how long will it take him to save
   £10.00?   _____ weeks

5 How many times can I take 20 from 200?   _____

6 A clock is 12 minutes fast. What is the correct time
   when the clock shows 10:25?   _____ : _____

7 Find the **sum** of all the even numbers between 1 and 9.   _____

○ 4

8 There are 85 children in Classes 1, 2 and 3. If there are 28 in
   Class 1, and 27 in Class 2, how many are there in Class 3? _____

9 How many are there in Classes 2 and 3 together?   _____

10 How many are there in Classes 1 and 2 together?   _____

○ 3

Here are the marks some children got in the last three spelling tests
(out of 10).

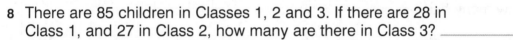

	Andrea	Mark	Deborah	Stuart	Alison	Steven
Test 1	7	8	9	7	8	9
Test 2	4	6	8	5	7	6
Test 3	9	10	8	7	9	7
Totals	20	24	25	19	22	22

11 Who had the highest total marks?   _____

12 Who had the lowest total marks?   _____

13 Who got fewer than 8 marks in each of the tests?   _____

14 Who got 8 or more marks in each of the tests?   _____

15 Who got 10 in one test?   _____

16 Who had fewer than 5 marks in one test?   _____

17–18 _____ and _____ got the same total marks.

Look at the **pictogram** and answer the questions.

Roundabouts	☺ ☺ ☺ ☺ ☺ ☺ ☺ ☺ ☺
Scenic Railway	☺ ☺ ☺ ☺ ☺ ☺ ☺ ☺
Dodgems	☺ ☺ ☺ ☺ ☺ ☺ ☺ ☺ ☺ ☺ ☺
Swing-boats	☺ ☺ ☺ ☺ ☺ ☺
Go Karts	☺ ☺ ☺ ☺

Key

☺ represents
2 people

19 How many more children went on the dodgems than on the swing-boats?   _____

20 There were _____ fewer children on the go karts than on the roundabouts.

21 How many children went on the scenic railway?   _____

22 What was the total number of children who went on these amusements?   _____

Maria is 131.5 cm tall. Susan is 3.25 cm shorter than Maria.
Cathy is 4.75 cm taller than Maria.

23 How tall is Susan?   _____ cm

24 How tall is Cathy?   _____ cm

A 1½ litres B 1¼ litres C 1 litre D 2¼ litres E 2½ litres

25–26 Jug _____ holds the most and jug _____ holds the least.

27–28 Jug _____ holds exactly twice as much as jug _____.

29 A beaker holds $\frac{1}{8}$ litre. How many beakers full of water can be poured from jug A? _____

30 What is the total amount that all the jugs will hold? _____ ◯ 6

July					
Sunday		5	12	19	26
Monday		6	13	20	27
Tuesday		7	14	21	28
Wednesday	1	8	15	22	29
Thursday	2	9	16	23	30
Friday	3	10	17	24	31
Saturday	4	11	18	25	

31 If today's date is July 3rd, what will be the date in one week's time? _____

32 What is the date on the third Tuesday in July? _____

33 How many days appear 5 times in this July? _____

34 A fortnight before July 25th is _____ ◯ 4

Fill in the missing numbers in each line.

35–36   1½   3   4½   _____   7½   9   _____   12

37–38   115   119   _____   127   _____   135   139

39–40   36   33   30   _____   _____   21   18   ◯ 6

Paper 21

Write these times for the 24-hour clock.

1 5 p.m.   ____ : ____   2 11 p.m.   ____ : ____

3 9:05 p.m.   ____ : ____   4 4:22 p.m.   ____ : ____

5 2:51 p.m.   ____ : ____   6 6:30 p.m.   ____ : ____

7 8:45 a.m.   ____ : ____   8 10:10 a.m.   ____ : ____   ◯ 8

9 What number needs to go in the box?

$2341 = 2000 + 300 + 40 +$ [   ]   ◯ 1

10 A ladder is 236 cm long, which is _____ cm to the nearest 10 cm.

11 Two ladders are _____ cm to the nearest 100 cm.   ◯ 2

12 A chocolate biscuit lasts Amy 55 seconds, which is _____ seconds
to the nearest 10 seconds.

13 How long will it take her to eat 4 at the same speed,
to the nearest 100 seconds?   _____   ◯ 2

14 What needs to be added/subtracted to change 8621 to 8221?   _____

15 What number will divide 33 and 44?   _____   ◯ 2

16–21 Here is part of a tables chart. Complete the empty brackets.

×			
	20	( )	24
	( )	33	( )
	( )	44	48
	50	( )	( )

◯ 6

22 How many pence in £14.74?   _____

23 How many pence in £100.30?   _____

24 How many pence in £60.02?   _____

25 How many pence in £0.02?   _____   ◯ 4

26–28 Which of these numbers are exactly **divisible** by 9? Underline them.

15   24   36   46   54   62   72   84   95   98   107

(3)

29–31 Colour in any **octagons** below.

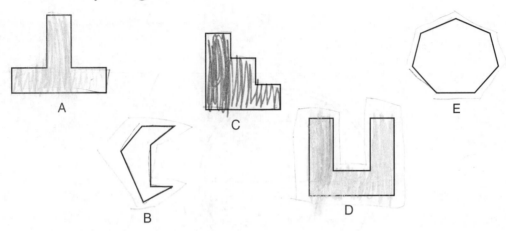

A   C   E

B   D

32 Tickets for a concert cost £9.
How many tickets can I buy with £60?

(3)

Twenty-five children are going to a swimming pool by a minibus which can take 11 passengers.

33 How many trips must the minibus make?

(2)

34 Write the correct number in the box.

450   → 25 less is | 425 |

(1)

35 Draw a circle around the lowest temperature: ⁻7°C   ⁻9°C

36 Draw a circle around the lowest temperature: ⁻31°C   ⁻30°C

(2)

Put a ring round the smallest and underline the largest in each line.

37–38 5412   1452   4251   2415   2514   5214

39–40 8426   4862   6824   8642   6842   4682

(4)

Paper 22

Fill in the missing numbers in each line.

1–2	34	28	23	19	___	14	___
3–4	___	9	11	10	12	11	13	___
5–7	$3\frac{1}{2}$	$7\frac{1}{2}$	___	$15\frac{1}{2}$	___	$23\frac{1}{2}$	___

7

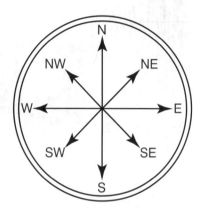

Can you name these compass points?

8 90° clockwise from N is _____

9 90° anticlockwise from SW is _____

10 2 right-angles clockwise from S is _____

11 3 right-angles anticlockwise from SW is _____

12 2 right-angles anticlockwise from SE is _____

13 2 right-angles clockwise from NW is _____

6

14 If a goldfish costs £1.25, how many can I buy for £6.25? _____

1

15 What is the **area** of rectangle B? ___ m²

16 What is the **perimeter** of rectangle B? ___ m

2

Complete the following lines.

17–18	80	40	20	_____	_____
19–20	12	23	34	_____	_____
21–22	60	80	100	_____	_____
23–24	20	17	14	_____	_____

8

Write the correct fraction in its lowest form in each space.

25 Dotted   _____

26 White   _____

27 Dotted   _____

28 White   _____

29 Dotted   _____

30 White   _____

6

31–35 A class of 36 children voted for their favourite school dinners and then made a chart.

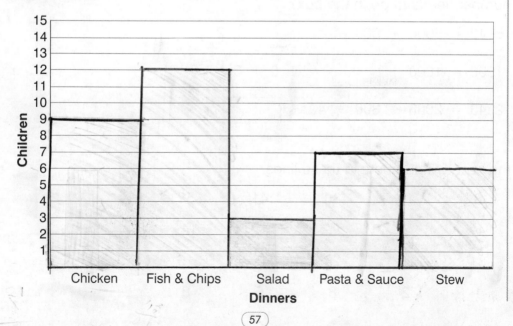

Shade in the columns to show how they voted:

- 3 children voted for salad.

- 3 times as many voted for chicken.

- One third of the class voted for fish and chips.

- The number who voted for stew was one half of the number who voted for fish and chips.

- Both sets of twins in the class, plus two other children, voted for pasta and sauce.

36 The most popular school dinner was _____

37 The least popular school dinner was _____ 〇 7

38 Write in figures nine thousand, two hundred and four. _____

39 Write in figures five thousand and seventy-five. _____

40 The TV programme lasted 138 minutes, which is _____ min to the nearest 10 min. 〇 3

Now go to the Progress Chart to record your score! **Total** 〇 40

Paper 23

What number needs to go in the box?

1 $5842 = 5000 + 800 + \boxed{} + 2$

2 $1906 = 1000 + \boxed{} + 0 + 6$

3 $2340 = 2000 + 300 + 40 + \boxed{}$ 〇 3

Write the next two numbers in these lines.

4	8	19	30	41	52	_____	_____
5	$4\frac{1}{2}$	7	$9\frac{1}{2}$	12	$14\frac{1}{2}$	_____	_____
6	31	27	23	19	15	_____	_____
7–8	1	2	3	5	8	_____	_____

〇 5

9–15 Complete the following sales board.

SALE	
Ordinary price	Half price
£9.80	
£5.20	
	£2.90
£7.40	
	£2.60
£10.20	
	£4.70

Underline the numbers which are divisible by 3.

| 16–18 | 69 | 101 | 58 | 405 | 521 | 3 |
| 19–20 | 602 | 73 | 237 | 35 | 852 | 484 |

Write the name **semicircle**, **equilateral triangle**, **isosceles triangle**, **quadrilateral**, **pentagon**, **hexagon**, **heptagon**, **cube**, **tetrahedron** or **parallelogram** under the correct shapes.

21
_____

22
_____

23
_____

24
_____

25
_____

26
_____

27
_____

28
_____

29
_____

30
_____

31
_____

32
_____

7

5

12

33 Which of the shapes on the page before has the
most edges? _____

34 James weighs 50 kg, which is ___ kg to the nearest 100 kg.

35–40 Put these numbers in order, largest to smallest.

3512	2531	3521	1523	2513	1532
___	___	___	___	___	___

Now go to the Progress Chart to record your score!   Total   **40**

Paper 24

1 From Applegate to Hampton (going through Beechton) is ___ km.

2 From Sheldon to Hampton (going through Maryland and Topstone) is
___ km.

3–4 The shortest journey from Maryland to Applegate goes through
_____ and is ___ km long.

5–6 The shortest journey from Beechton to Sheldon goes through
_____ and is ___ km long.

Look at this calculation carefully and use it to help you with the following questions.

$$27 + 21 \quad = 48$$

7 $127 + 121 = $ _____

8 $48 - 21 \quad = $ _____

9 $527 + 221 = $ _____

10 $248 - 21 \quad = $ _____ 4

Here is another example and set of questions.

$$52 + 16 \quad = 68$$

11 $252 + 116 = $ _____

12 $852 + 116 = $ _____

13 $68 - 16 \quad = $ _____

14 $768 - 216 = $ _____ 4

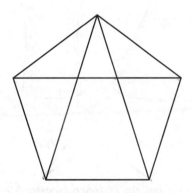

15 What is the name of the outside **polygon**? _____

16 How many **squares** can you find in the polygon? _____

17 What is the name of a polygon with seven sides? Heptagon 3

Fill in the missing numbers in each line.

18–19	$2\frac{1}{2}$	4	$5\frac{1}{2}$	7	_____ _____
20–21	33	_____	39	42 _____	48
22–23	_____	38	34	30	26 _____
24–25	2p	_____	8p	_____ 14p	17p

8

61

Southcross School has 4 half-hour lessons each morning.

26–34 The lessons start at 9:40 and there is a break of 20 minutes after the 2nd lesson. Fill in the timetable.

	Begins	Ends
First lesson	09:40	10:10
Second lesson	10:10	10:40
Break	10:40	11:00
Third lesson	11:00	11:30
Fourth lesson	11:30	12:00

9

A	B	C	D
1 litre	500 ml	250 ml	750 ml

35 How many times could you fill bottle C from bottle A? _____

36 Bottle A holds twice as much as bottle _____ .

37 Bottle D and bottle _____ together hold as much as A.

38 How much more does A hold than D? _____ ml

39 How many times could you fill C from D? _____

5

40 468 × 7 = _____

1

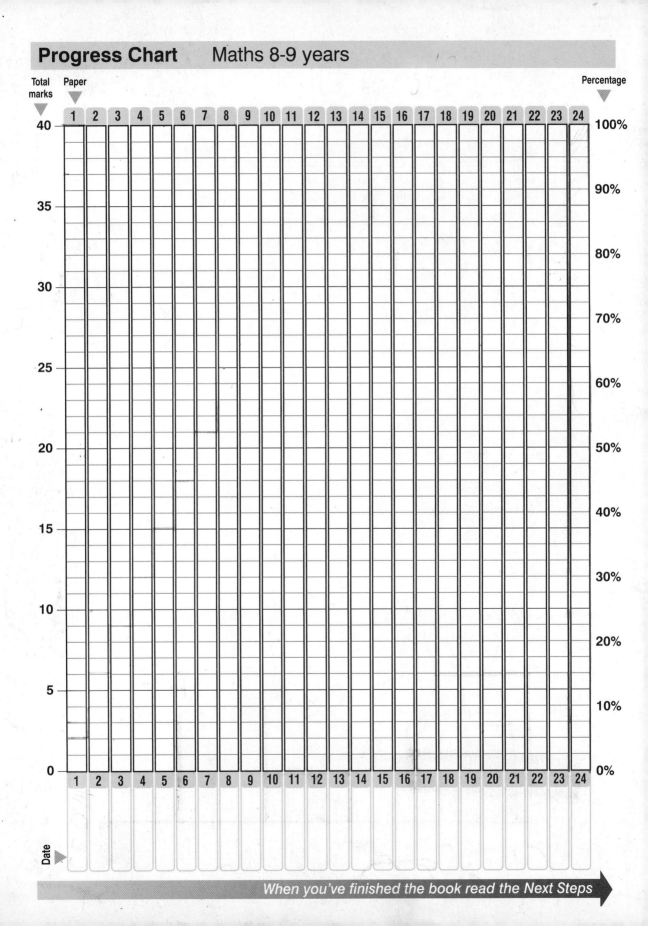

Progress Chart   Maths 8-9 years

When you've finished the book read the Next Steps